A Note to Parents

DK READERS is a compelling program for beginning readers, designed in conjunction with leading literacy experts, including Dr. Linda Gambrell, Distinguished Professor of Education at Clemson University. Dr. Gambrell has served as President of the National Reading Conference, the College Reading Association, and the International Reading Association.

Beautiful illustrations and superb full-color photographs combine with engaging, easy-to-read stories to offer a fresh approach to each subject in the series. Each DK READER is guaranteed to capture a child's interest while developing his or her reading skills, general knowledge, and love of reading.

The five levels of DK READERS are aimed at different reading abilities, enabling you to choose the books that are exactly right for your child:

Pre-level 1: Learning to read
Level 1: Beginning to read
Level 2: Beginning to read alone
Level 3: Reading alone
Level 4: Proficient readers

The "normal" age at which a child begins to read can be anywhere from three to eight years old. Adult participation through the lower levels is very helpful for providing encouragement, discussing storylines, and sounding out unfamiliar words.

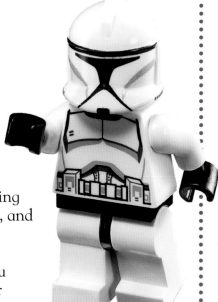

No matter which level you select, you can be sure that you are helping your child learn to read, then read to learn!

Editorial Assistant Ruth Amos
Senior Editor Elizabeth Dowsett
Editorial Coordinator Clare Millar
Designers Jon Hall, Sandra Perry, Jaynan Spengler
Senior Designer David McDonald
Slipcase Designer Mark Penfound
Pre-Production Producer Kavita Varma
Senior Producer Lloyd Robertson
Managing Editor Paula Regan
Design Managers Jo Connor, Guy Harvey
Creative Manager Sarah Harland
Art Director Lisa Lanzarini
Publisher Julie Ferris
Publishing Director Simon Beecroft

Reading Consultant
Linda B. Gambrell, Ph.D.

Dorling Kindersley would like to thank: Randi Sørensen and
Robert Stefan Ekblom at the LEGO Group and J. W. Rinzler,
Leland Chee, Troy Alders and Carol Roeder at Lucasfilm.

This edition published in 2017
First American edition, 2012
Published in the United States by DK Publishing
345 Hudson Street, New York, New York 10014
DK, a Division of Penguin Random House LLC

Page design copyright ©2017 Dorling Kindersley Limited

Slipcase UID: 001-307475-June/2017

A catalog record for this book is available
from the Library of Congress.

ISBN: 978-5-0010-1461-4

Printed and bound in China

www.LEGO.com
www.starwars.com
www.dk.com

A WORLD OF IDEAS:
SEE ALL THERE IS TO KNOW

Contents

4   Trouble in the galaxy

6   Welcome to the Jedi

8   Jedi protection

10   Assassin adventure

12   The clone army

14   Stop that bounty hunter!

16   The droid army

18   Dark secrets

20   Jedi to the rescue!

22   The Battle of Geonosis

24   Dooku's escape

26   Lightning duel

28   Dooku's master

30   Time to celebrate!

32   Quiz

DK READERS

BEGINNING TO READ ALONE

2

LEGO STAR WARS

ATTACK OF THE CLONES ™

Written by Elizabeth Dowsett

Trouble in the galaxy

Meet Count Dooku!
Once, Count Dooku protected
the galaxy, but now he is a
powerful Sith Lord.
The Sith are dangerous warriors
who are greedy and want power.

Count Dooku leads an evil
group called the Separatists.
The Separatists want to control
the galaxy.
They will fight anyone who
stands in their way.

Dark power

The Force is a form of energy. It can be used for good, but the Sith use the dark side of the Force for evil.

Welcome to the Jedi

These two Jedi are Obi-Wan Kenobi and Anakin Skywalker. The Jedi use the Force to protect the galaxy and keep peace.

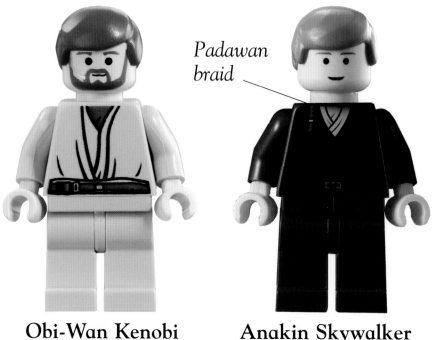

Padawan braid

Obi-Wan Kenobi   **Anakin Skywalker**

Obi-Wan is a wise Jedi Master. He is Anakin's teacher.

Anakin is Obi-Wan's Padawan.
He is learning to be a Jedi Knight.
Count Dooku used to be a
Jedi, too, but now he has turned
against the Jedi Order.

Jedi prefer to make peace
rather than fight their enemies.
If they must do battle, they use
powerful lightsabers.

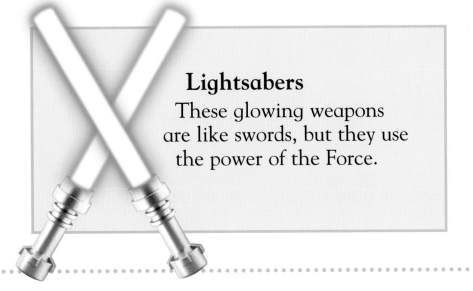

Lightsabers
These glowing weapons
are like swords, but they use
the power of the Force.

Jedi protection

Obi-Wan and Anakin have an important Jedi mission. They must protect Senator Padmé Amidala on the planet Coruscant.

Padmé may be in danger, but she is not afraid! She is very brave and daring.

The Senate

The Senate rules the Republic peacefully. The Senate is made up of a group of people who are called Senators.

Padmé and Anakin are childhood friends.

They are very happy to see each other after many years.

Zam Wesell's
green speeder

Assassin adventure

Help! Someone has tried
to attack Padmé.
Don't worry—Padmé is not hurt.

Obi-Wan and Anakin chase
after Padmé's attacker in a
yellow airspeeder.

Airspeeder

The Jedi are following an assassin called Zam Wesell. Before they catch Zam, someone destroys her.

Who destroyed Zam? The Jedi want to know!

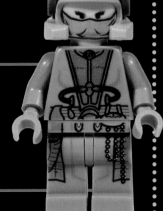

Secret assassin
Assassins are paid to secretly track down and attack people.

The clone army

Look! Obi-Wan has found
a huge army of soldiers.

These soldiers are identical
to one another because they are
human clones.
They are all copied from one
man named Jango Fett.

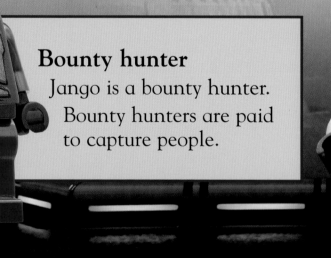

Bounty hunter
Jango is a bounty hunter.
Bounty hunters are paid
to capture people.

Jango wears blue armor,
but the clones wear white armor.
Under the armor, the clone
troopers all look like Jango.

The clone army will fight for
the Republic, but it is a secret.
Sshh! Don't tell anyone.

Stop that bounty hunter!

Obi-Wan has found out that it was Jango Fett who destroyed Zam Wesell.
Watch out, Obi-Wan!
Jango fires his blaster, but clever Obi-Wan uses his lightsaber as a shield.

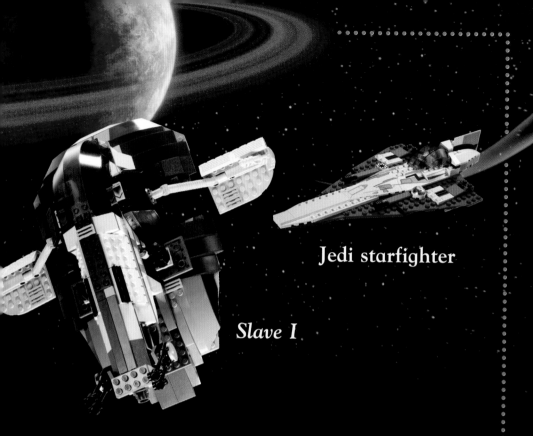

Jedi starfighter

Slave I

Jango escapes in his starship,
the *Slave I.* Whoosh!
Poor Obi-Wan doesn't like to fly,
but he chases after Jango in his
Jedi starfighter.
He follows Jango to a planet
called Geonosis.

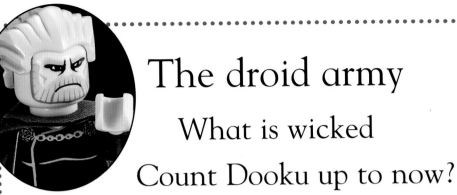

The droid army

What is wicked Count Dooku up to now? He is building an army of droids to fight for the Separatists!

The droids are metal soldiers. The smaller, yellow droids are called battle droids. They are not very smart.

Battle droid

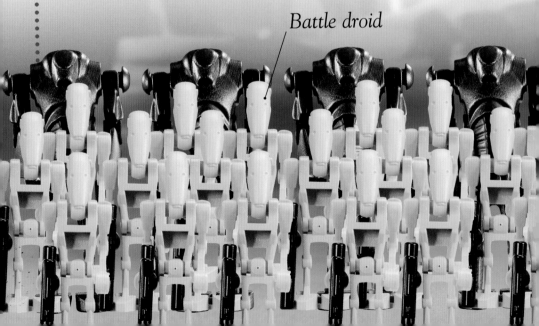

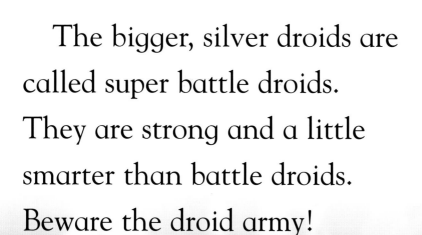

Geonosians

The droid army is made
by insect-like Geonosians.
They have large wings
and big eyes, like flies.

The bigger, silver droids are
called super battle droids.
They are strong and a little
smarter than battle droids.
Beware the droid army!

Super battle droid

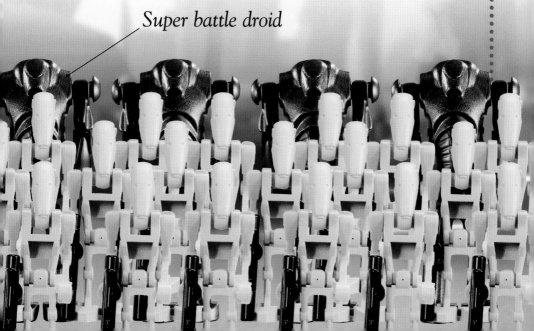

Dark secrets

Oh no! Count Dooku has found Obi-Wan on Geonosis and captured him! Energy beams keep Obi-Wan floating in a prison cell.

Count Dooku tells Obi-Wan that a clever Sith Lord has secretly taken control of the Republic.

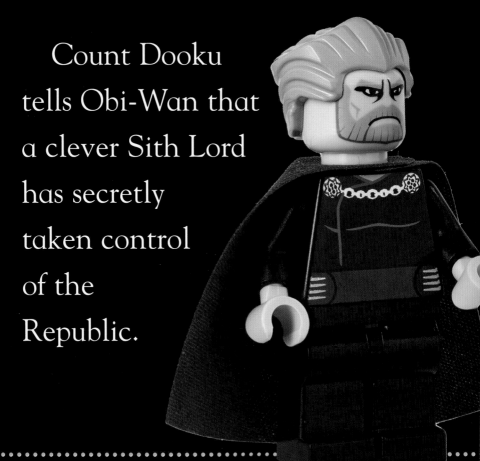

Dooku reveals
that it was this
mysterious Sith
who planned
the attack
on Padmé
Amidala.

Obi-Wan
cannot move
his arms
or legs.
He is trapped!

Jedi to the rescue!

Anakin and Padmé come
to save Obi-Wan, but the
Separatists capture them, too!

More Jedi arrive, led by Jedi
Master Mace Windu.
The Jedi rescue their friends,
but then the droid army attacks!

Mace
Windu

Jedi strike
team

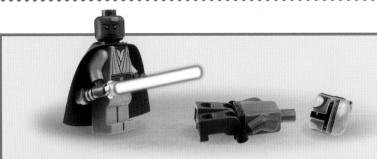

Jedi warrior

Skilled Jedi Master Mace Windu defeats
Jango Fett with his purple lightsaber.
The bounty hunter is finished, but lots of
Separatists still want to fight.

The Jedi fight bravely, but
there are too many battle droids.
Help! The Jedi are surrounded.

Droid army

Republic
gunship

The Battle of Geonosis

Look! The clone troopers have
arrived in a Republic gunship.
They will rescue the Jedi!

The clone army launches
an attack on the droids and
the Geonosians,
who fight
back!

Geonosian cannon

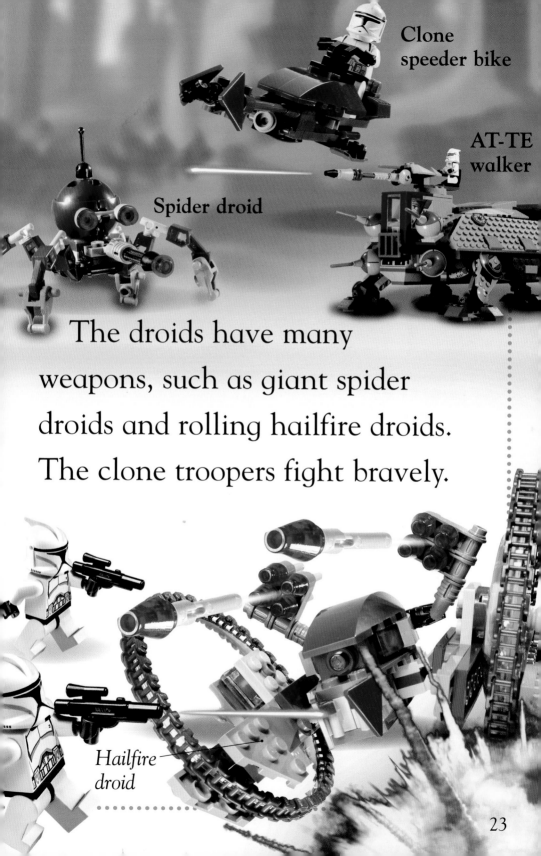

Clone
speeder bike

AT-TE
walker

Spider droid

The droids have many
weapons, such as giant spider
droids and rolling hailfire droids.
The clone troopers fight bravely.

*Hailfire
droid*

Speeder bike

Geonosian guard

Dooku's escape

Who is this running away
from the battle?
It is cowardly Count Dooku,
fleeing on his speeder bike.
Quick, the villain will escape!

Obi-Wan and Anakin follow
Count Dooku to a secret hangar.

Anakin attacks the evil
Count, but he is overpowered.
Obi-Wan then fights Dooku
in a tense lightsaber battle,
but Dooku is too powerful.
All seems lost!

to Anakin's rescue, just in time!
This is Yoda, Grand Master of
all the Jedi.
He might be very old and small,
but he is very powerful.
Do not judge him
by his size!

Yoda uses the
Force to leap
and spin
around Dooku.

Count Dooku attacks Yoda with crackling Sith lightning, but Yoda is strong enough to bounce it back to him!

See the lightning flash!

Dooku's master

Count Dooku is powerful,
but he is not as powerful as Yoda.

The Sith Lord knows he
cannot win his duel against
Yoda, so he runs away!
Dooku uses his Solar
Sailer spacecraft to
fly to Coruscant.

Solar Sailer

Now Count Dooku has a secret meeting with a mysterious, cloaked figure.

This is Dooku's Sith master. He uses the dark side of the Force to hide his identity from the Jedi.

His name is Darth Sidious, but who is he? Where did he come from?

Time to celebrate!

The Battle of Geonosis is over and Count Dooku has fled! Also, Anakin and Padmé have fallen in love.

It is against the Jedi laws to get married, but they have a secret wedding.

C-3PO

Their droids, C-3PO and R2-D2, are the only guests.

The Jedi have won the battle this time, but the Clone Wars have only just begun.
Who is Darth Sidious and when will he strike next?

R2-D2

Quiz

1. What is this fly-like creature called?

2. What type of droid is this?

3. What is the name of Jango Fett's starship?

4. Who is this green warrior?

5. Who flees in the Solar Sailer spacecraft?

1. A Geonosian, 2. Super battle droid, 3. Slave I, 4. Yoda, 5. Count Dooku